LOVING GOD

STUDY·GUIDE

LOVING GOD

GOD

STUDY•GUIDE

CHARLES COLSON

Zondervan Books
Zondervan Publishing House
Grand Rapids, Michigan

Acknowledgements: This study guide was written by
Art Lindsley and Anita Moreland with contributions from
Dr. Carl F. H. Henry, Charles W. Colson, Ellen Santilli,
and Whitney Kuniholm.

© Copyright 1983 by Fellowship Communications, P.O. Box 17500, Washington, D.C. 20041.
Reproduction of the whole or any part of the contents without
written permission is prohibited.

Zondervan Books are published by Zondervan Publishing House,
1415 Lake Drive, S.E., Grand Rapids, Michigan 49506

Quotations from the text of Loving God used by permission of Zondervan Publishing House

Printed in the United States of America

84 85 86 87 88 89 90 / 10 9 8 7 6 5 4 3 2 1

CONTENTS

Introduction: How to Use this Book   V

Chapter 1: Losing and Gaining   1

Chapter 2: Obedience and Faith   7

Chapter 3: What is the Bible?   13

Chapter 4: The Cost of Discipleship   19

Chapter 5: The Sin in Us   25

Chapter 6: "... When You Come Into Your Kingdom"   31

Chapter 7: Salt and Light   37

Chapter 8: Justice, Kindness, Humility   43

Chapter 9: Taking a Stand   49

Chapter 10: A Fellowship of Suffering   55

Chapter 11: The Visible Church   61

Chapter 12: Death Into Life   67

Chapter 13: Living in the Arena   73

Summary Statement   79

Action Statement   80

Introduction

This companion study guide for Charles Colson's third book, *Loving God*, is designed to help you interact with the issues and ideas the book raises. *Loving God* wraps its teaching in stories and anecdotes; the studies in this volume will assist you as you reflect on the stories and their underlying lessons.

There is no issue more critical to Christians than knowing how to live in love, obedience and a growing relationship with the living God. Whether you plan to study in a group or individually, this booklet, along with *Loving God* and your Bible, will guide you in your search for a more intimate bond with your Lord. Each chapter of the study guide focuses on a theme from *Loving God*, highlighting first the issue or idea in general, then on how it applies to everyday life.

Personal Study

As you read *Loving God* and reflect on the book's issues, this guide will hopefully serve as a catalyst for further thought and personal application. *Loving God* is by no means the final word on the substantive issues of the Christian life — faith, repentance, obedience, holiness — but it is written to provoke thought and in-depth study of the Scriptures themselves.

As you use this guide, set aside time, a copy of *Loving God*, a Bible, notebook and a pen. Be sure to read the selections from *Loving God* and the Bible that are indicated at the beginning of each study chapter. If time allows, read the supplemental Scripture readings as well — they'll give you a more in-depth perspective.

If you have any questions about any of the issues or questions raised in this study, be sure to discuss them with a Christian friend, your pastor or leader in your church.

Group Study

This study is also suited to groups. Divided into 13 chapters, it fits into a Sunday School quarter, or can easily be adapted to a weekly Bible study or home group.

Preparation is essential for a group study. Before coming together for discussion, everyone in the group should be familiar with Scripture passages and *Loving God* chapters so the group can delve into discussion.

Leaders for group studies should read at least one week ahead in both *Loving God* and the Study Guide in order to add discussion topics that will make each study specifically applicable. In the study focusing on sharing the suffering of others, for example, leaders might consider inviting a guest speaker involved in an active local ministry to address the group. Or, in studies dealing with the quest for God, perhaps group members would want to share their personal testimonies. Or, individuals in the group can read some of the books suggested for further study, and then report back to the rest of the group. Think creatively how to use this book and adapt its teachings to the specific needs and areas of growth of your group.

Study Structure

Each of the 13 study chapters follow the same format. The framework provides a structure for organization, but should be adapted and used to fit the character of your particular group. The eight-part study format includes:

INTRODUCTION — A few sentences sketching out the study topic, serving as a transition from the text to the study, and from one study to the next.

READ — *Loving God* and Scripture portions that serve as background material, divided into main and supplemental readings. The main readings are essential; supplemental readings are important in that they provide a broader context and a more in-depth perspective.

STUDY — The first set of study questions covers factual material from *Loving God* and the main Scripture readings. Questions are geared to begin examination of each topic in general terms.

REFLECT — The second set of questions focuses in more personally and is designed to make readers think in relation to the content to their lives. Your responses aren't necessarily right or wrong. This section is meant to be a time of reflection for each person involved in the study, to see how

God would have you apply the ideas and issues *Loving God* examines.

SUMMARIZE — This section allows space for each reader to capsulize the most important lesson learned from the study.

APPLY — This follow-up section encourages the reader to apply the lessons learned in the arena of everyday experience. It is important to be specific here, to state when and how you plan to act. Also, as you go through each of the 13 studies, take time to check back to previous application sections to monitor your progress.

PRAYER — Each study ends with prayer, focusing on the topics and themes of that chapter at hand. Of course this is a starting point for your prayer. You will naturally want to go on to praise, thanksgiving, confession and intercession as necessary.

FURTHER STUDY — A list of suggested readings is provided for those interested in reading more about particular topics. The lists are by no means exhaustive, but provide several suggestions for additional study.

The 13 chapters provided in this volume are prayerfully designed to help you explore the Scriptures to find what God has to say about the radical truths of the Christian life, and how they apply in your personal walk with God and commitment to Him. Ideally, this study should serve as a trigger for confronting areas of needed change and growth, as well as the means by which you root yourself deeper in the rich treasure of the Scriptures and life in Christ.

1
Losing and Gaining

Few of Christ's teachings are more difficult to comprehend than His statement that the only way to find one's life is to lose it for His sake. It is imperative, however, that Christians understand this crucial paradox of the faith — and then live it. For it is the first step in living one's life for Christ, the beginning of the pilgrimage toward loving God.

Our commitment to Him is half-hearted if we seek to live it out only on our terms. Living on His terms can be costly, of course, but the crucial step for the obedient Christian is to make that choice in the midst of a culture more preoccupied with self-indulgence than sacrifice.

Tough though it is, that obedience is demanded of us. The Scriptures as well as the lives of Christian disciples through the centuries echo the true victory of lives submitted totally to the Lordship of Christ.

READ

Main Readings:

Loving God: Introduction,
   Chapter 1, and Chapter 2

Matthew 10:38, 39; 16:24, 25

Luke 14:27; 17:33

John 12:24-26

Supplemental Readings:

Philippians 3:1-11

John 8:31, 32, 36

Romans 12:1, 2

Matthew 6:19-24

STUDY

1. Describe the characteristics of Boris Kornfeld's life. What events showed he had lost his life for Christ? _____

_____

_____

_____

2. What examples of this do you find in society today? In the established church? Among your Christian friends? ___

_____

_____

_____

"It is vain, O men, that you seek within yourselves the cure for your miseries. All your insight only leads you to the knowledge that it is not in yourselves that you will discover the pure and the good."

Blaise Pascal (introduction)

3. What is society's ideal for living a good life? How is a life lost for Christ different from this ideal? _____

_____

_____

_____

4. In what ways did Boris Kornfeld lack freedom prior to his knowledge of Christ? _____

_____

_____

_____

5. After Kornfeld came to believe Christ, how did he come to experience freedom? _____

_____

_____

_____

6. What are some of the things people mean when they refer to the "victorious Christian life?" Is there a difference between this and a life lost for Christ? Explain. _____

_____

_____

_____

_____

7. What does losing one's life for Christ have to do with loving God? _____

_____

_____

_____

REFLECT

1. Think about a typical week in your life. What four or five activities take up most of your time? _____

_____

_____

_____

What does this say about your priorities? _____

_____

_____

_____

2. Think about the *process* of Kornfeld's turn to obedience. What do you see as the turning point? In what situations in your own life are you presented with similar choices? _____

_____

_____

"If anyone wishes to come after me, let him deny himself, and take up his cross, and follow me. For whoever wishes to save his life shall lose it; but whoever loses his life for my sake and the gospel's shall save it."

Mark 8:34, 35

3

"It is not
what we do
that matters,
but what a
sovereign God
chooses to do
through us."

Loving God,
page 25

3.   Identify some men and women from the Bible whose lives illustrate the paradox of losing one's life for Christ to find it. _____

_____

_____

_____

_____

4.   What are common characteristics of these people? ____

_____

_____

_____

_____

5.   Would living the paradox, like these examples did, change *your* life? Explain. _____

_____

_____

_____

_____

6.   Have there been times when you've tried to "save" your life? Describe them. _____

_____

_____

_____

7.   In what ways could you "lose" your life for Christ's sake
and the Gospel in the next year? _____

_____

_____

_____

_____

"But,
paradoxically,
along with . . .
anxiety came
tremendous
freedom.

SUMMARIZE

Having
accepted the
possibility of
death, Boris
Kornfeld was
now free to
live."

Loving God,
page 32

What is the most significant lesson you have learned from
this study? _____

_____

_____

_____

APPLY

How and when will you apply what you have learned in this
study in thought, word or action? _____

_____

_____

_____

_____

PRAY

Talk to God about one or two aspects of your life that
you are reluctant to lose for Christ's sake. Ask the
Holy Spirit to strengthen you as you seek to take the
commands of Jesus seriously and to live them.

FURTHER STUDY

Dietrich Bonhoeffer, *The Cost of Discipleship,* MacMillan Publishing Company, Inc., 1963.

H. Fairlie, *Seven Deadly Sins Today,* Notre Dame, 1979.

Douglas Hyde, *Dedication and Leadership,* Notre Dame, 1966.

John Murray, *Principles of Conduct,* Wm. B. Eerdmans Publishing Company, 1957. (Especially the chapter on freedom).

Paul Vitz, *Psychology as Religion,* Wm. B. Eerdmans Publishing Company, 1977.

"*Empowering the Self: A Look at the Human Potential Movement,*" SCP *Journal,* Winter 1981-82. (P.O. Box 2418, Berkeley, CA 94702).

Alexander Solzhenitsyn, *Gulag Archipelago II,* Harper & Row, 1974.

NOTES

2
Obedience and Faith

Two of the words most often used in the Christian Church are faith and obedience. These are essential building blocks, the very steps by which the Christian walks with his Lord. And they grow out of one another — as we believe God at His Word, we act upon that belief. It's an interrelationship of head and heart that compels the believer to passionate discipline — a single-minded desire to please the God we love.

That desire can lead the Christian to actions the world may call radical. Certainly that was the case with the disciples after their encounter with the risen Christ — believing Christ to be the Son of God, they went out, in obedience to His Word, and changed their world.

That same certainty of faith and fervent obedience should characterize the lives of those who follow the risen Christ today.

READ

Main Readings:

Loving God: Chapter 3

Hebrews 11

Matthew 8

Supplemental Readings:

Luke 7

John 14:15

Job 13:15

I Samuel 15:22

I John 5:3-5

I Corinthians 16:13

Galatians 2:20

Acts 5:27-29

Isaiah 1:16-20

Deuteronomy 11:26-29

STUDY

1. How was Boris Kornfeld's faith evident? In what ways was he obedient? _____

_____

_____

2. What is your definition of faith? Of obedience? What is the relationship between the two? _____

*"Blessed is he
who has
not seen
and yet
believed."*

John 20:29

3. How does one know when and how to obey God? Cite examples from your own life. _____

_____

_____

_____

4. Should obedience ever be "blind?" When? Why should one obey even when the results are not clear? _____

_____

_____

_____

5. Why do you think God often does not allow us to see the results of our obedience? _____

_____

_____

_____

6. What is God's attitude toward the worship of disobedient people? (Amos 5) _____

_____

_____

_____

7. What are some proper and improper motives for obedience to God? _____

_____

_____

_____

_____

REFLECT

1. What are some instances in which you have acted as if God did not exist? _____

_____

_____

_____

2. Do you find obedience to the Lord difficult? When and why? Can you remember times when it was easier? Describe the difference. _____

_____

_____

_____

_____

".. .*Christianity must evoke from the believer the same response it drew from the first disciples: a passionate desire to obey and please God . . . That is the beginning of loving God."*

Loving God, page 40.

3. Think about times when you have had faith in God. What motivated you to have such faith? What were the results of that faith? _____

_____

_____

_____

_____

4. Describe some results of obedience to God in your life. __

_____

_____

_____

_____

5. Is it possible to have faith, but not be obedient? Or, to be obedient, but not have faith? Explain. _____

"This is real faith: believing and acting obediently regardless of circumstances or contrary to evidence."

Loving God, *page 37.*

_____

_____

_____

_____

Do you think you exhibit enough of both in your life? _____

_____

_____

_____

6. Why are faith and obedience important? _____

_____

_____

_____

7. How do faith and obedience in your life relate to loving God? _____

_____

_____

_____

_____

SUMMARIZE

What is the most significant lesson you have learned from this study? _____

_____

_____

_____

_____

APPLY

How and when will you apply what you have learned in this study in thought, word or action? _____

_____

_____

_____

_____

PRAY

Think of one area of your life where you need greater faith and another where you need more disciplined obedience. Spend time praying about these.

FURTHER STUDY

J. I. Packer, *Knowing God*, Inter-Varsity Press, 1973.

S. Charnock (1628-1680) *The Existence and Attributes of God*, (Reprinted by Sovereign Grace, 1958).

J. G. Machen, *What is Faith?*, Wm. B. Eerdmans, 1962.

Alexander Solzhenitsyn, *Gulag Archipelago* II, Harper & Row, 1974.

NOTES

3
What is the Bible?

Too often, we have a head knowledge of the Bible, but fail to immerse ourselves fully in the Word, believe it and stake our very lives on its integrity.

But God's Word has a power and authority that must be incorporated into the believer, that must dictate thoughts, belief and action. It is not a collection of pious sayings, but a lamp, truth, a two-edged sword that penetrates the core of who we are and can be used by God to utterly transform us from within.

Our attitude toward God's Word is, like faith and obedience, integral to our growth in Him. If we claim to follow Christ, then we must treat the Scriptures as He did, risking our lives on their authenticity and truth.

READ

Main Readings:

Loving God: Chapter 4,
    Chapter 5, Chapter 6 and
    Chapter 7

Romans 13:12, 13

Psalm 19:7-11

Matthew 5:17-19; 28:18

Supplementary Readings:

Luke 24:22

I Corinthians 15:3-8, 17, 19, 32

Luke 4:18-21

John 5:39; 17:17

Matthew 4

Luke 4

Deuteronomy 8:3; 6:16

STUDY

1. What was Augustine like before he found God? What were the high points of his search for God? _____

_____

_____

_____

_____

2. How is Augustine like 20th century people on the same search? _____

_____

_____

_____

"The relativism of the modern mind-set is loathe to subscribe to the absolute authority of anything, and that attitude has seeped into our perspective, resulting in a barrage of questions, attacks, and rewrites of the Scriptures."

Loving God, page 72.

3. What elements of Augustine's story relate to our discussion of faith and obedience? _____

_____

_____

_____

4. How does Augustine's story illustrate the power of Scripture? _____

_____

_____

_____

5. Is the way one views the Scriptures important to conversion? Why or why not? _____

_____

_____

_____

6. Describe your perspective on how Watergate relates to the authority of Scripture. _____

_____

_____

_____

7. What was Christ's view of Scripture? _____

_____

_____

_____

_____

"The Bible's power rests upon the fact that it is the reliable, errorless, and infallible Word of God."

Loving God,
page 56.

8. How would you respond to each of the criticisms of the Bible that appear on pages 72-74 of *Loving God*? _____

_____

_____

_____

_____

REFLECT

1. What adjectives would you use to describe the power of Scripture as you have experienced it in your life? _____

_____

_____

_____

2. Describe your search for God. _____

_____

_____

_____

_____

How did the Bible influence your search? _____

_____

_____

3. How does Augustine's search for God compare and contrast with yours? _____

_____

_____

4. Describe times in your life when God's Word has made a critical difference in your decision-making. What major decisions do you now face? How might God's Word assist you? _____

_____

_____

_____

5. What is the most common criticism your non-Christian friends make of the Bible? _____

_____

_____

How do you respond? _____

_____

_____

6. Your personal view of Scripture is: _____

_____

_____

Your view is important because: _____

_____

_____

_____

SUMMARIZE

What is the most significant lesson you have learned from this study? _____

_____

_____

_____

_____

APPLY

How and when will you apply what you have learned in this study in thought, word or action? _____

_____

_____

_____

_____

". . . Nothing has affected the rise and fall of civilization, the character of cultures, the structure of governments, and the lives of the inhabitants of this planet as profoundly as the words of the Bible."

Loving God, page 55.

PRAY

Ask God to give you a greater hunger for His Word and for increased diligence in spending time reading and studying it daily.

FURTHER STUDY

James Montgomery Boice, ed., *Does Inerrancy Matter?*, International Council on Biblical Inerrancy (P.O. Box 13261, Oakland, Calif. 94661), 1979.

F. F. Bruce, *New Testament Documents — Are They Reliable?*, Wm. B. Eerdmans, 1959.

R. T. France, *Jesus and the Old Testament*, Inter-Varsity Press, 1972.

Richard C. Halverson, *The Timelessness of Christ*, Regal Books, 1982.

Josh McDowell, *Evidence that Demands a Verdict*, volumes I and II, Campus Crusade, 1979.

John W. Montgomery, ed., *God's Inerrant Word: An International Symposium on the Trustworthiness of Scripture*, Bethany House, 1974.

J. I. Packer, *God Has Spoken*, Inter-Varsity Press, 1979.

John K. Ryan, trans., *Confessions of St. Augustine*, Doubleday, 1960.

R. C. Sproul, *Knowing Scripture*, Inter-Varsity Press, 1977.

John Walvoord, *Inspiration and Interpretation*, Wm. B. Eerdmans, 1957.

NOTES

_____

_____

_____

_____

_____

_____

_____

_____

_____

_____

4
The Cost of Discipleship

Jesus never minimizes the cost of discipleship. He is not desperate to get followers at any cost. In fact, as you read the gospels, you will find that Jesus often seems to discourage people from following — at least until they understand and experience the reality of repentance and obedience. He insists that people know what the Christian life will cost.

Repentance involves turning away from the old and choosing a whole new style of life with different values and priorities. We cannot be followers of Christ on our own terms, commitment to Him is an all-or-nothing proposition that radically alters the totality of one's life.

READ

Main Readings:

Loving God Chapter 8 and Chapter 9

Luke 9:57-62; 14:28-35

Matthew 10

Supplementary Readings:

Luke 11:27-54

Matthew 3:7-12; 19:21-30

Mark 18:34-38

Philippians 3:7-11

Isaiah 29:13, 14

STUDY

1. Describe Mickey Cohen's encounter with Christianity. (*Loving God*, pp. 85-92) _____ _____

_____

_____

_____

2. What was Mickey Cohen's understanding of Christianity? (*Loving God*, pp. 85-92) _____

_____

_____

_____

"No one, after putting his hand to the plow and looking back, is fit for the Kingdom of God."

Luke 9:62

3. Did the Christians who talked with Mickey about Christ explain all he needed to know? How would you have explained things differently? _____

_____

_____

_____

_____

4. What was Mickey's mistake? _____

_____

_____

_____

5. What do you think went through Mickey's mind when he considered, then rejected, Christ? _____

_____

_____

_____

_____

_____

6. For you, what is the relationship of repentance to discipleship? _____

_____

_____

_____

_____

_____

7. What are some obvious changes that should take place in a person when there is true repentance? (Galatians 5:13-26; Romans 12) _____

_____

_____

_____

"Repentance is much more than self-flagellation, more than regret, more than deep sorrow for past sins . . ."

Loving God, *page 94.*

REFLECT

1. How are you like Mickey Cohen? _____

_____

_____

2. Describe what happens when you repent: your convictions, your feelings, your attitudes, your reactions. Have you ever made repentance that was insincere? When, and with what results? _____

_____

_____

_____

_____

3. What was the most difficult thing for you to surrender to Christ as you become a true disciple? Are you currently holding back anything that God wants you to let go of? What is it and why is it difficult to surrender? _____

_____

_____

_____

_____

4. How do *you* know you are a disciple of Christ? How do *others* know? _____

_____

_____

_____

5. Describe your own discipleship. What has your faith in Jesus cost you? _____

". . . when he becomes guilty . . . he shall confess that in which he has sinned."

Leviticus 5:5

_____

_____

_____

_____

SUMMARIZE

What is the most significant lesson you have learned from this study? _____

_____

_____

_____

APPLY

How and when will you apply what you have learned in this study in thought, word or action? _____

_____

_____

_____

_____

_____

"The call to repentance — individual and corporate — is one of the most consistent themes of Scripture."

Loving God, *page 94.*

PRAY

Think of one area in your life where you are holding back from giving God complete control. Honestly admit to God your fears and concerns about this area; ask the Holy Spirit to give you the courage and determination to totally surrender it.

FURTHER STUDY

Dietrich Bonhoeffer, *The Cost of Discipleship,* Macmillan, 1963. (see section on Luke 9:57-62)

Mickey Cohen, *In My Own Words: The Underworld Autobiography of Michael Mickey Cohen* as told to John Peer Nugent, Englewood Cliffs, New Jersey, Prentice-Hall, 1975.

Curtis Mitchell, *Billy Graham: Saint or Sinner,* Revell, 1979.

John Murray, *Redemption: Accomplished and Applied,* Wm. B. Eerdmans, 1955. (see chapter on repentance)

David Myers, *The Inflated Self,* Seabury Press, 1980.

Foy Valentine, *What do You do After You Say Amen?,* Word, 1980.

J. W. Wenham, *Christ and the Bible,* Inter-Varsity Press, 1973.

NOTES

5
The Sin in Us

Many Christians neglect teaching or thinking about repentance today. First, it is an unpleasant message. It is far easier to focus only on peace, love, joy and forgiveness. And second, we have difficulty seeing and admitting our sin. It is easy to deceive ourselves.

But the fact is we are not by nature morally neutral. We are inclined toward sin. When restraints are withdrawn, people inevitably choose evil. Even in the case of believers, a battle between good and evil is being waged in every heart.

God's standard of goodness includes not only the external action, but also the internal motive. An outwardly good action can be performed so others will notice and applaud. When we take into account both action and motive, we can see why the Bible says there is "none who does good."

True repentance is a change that occurs from the inside out. It is not enough to simply change outward actions, or to appear to be good. A vital life in Christ can only be lived when actions flow from a heart that has been changed through full acceptance and trust in Christ's death on the cross.

READ

Main Readings:

Loving God: Chapter 10

Jeremiah 17:5-11

Mark 7:1-23

Supplementary Readings:

I John 1:5-10

James 1:23, 24

Romans 3:10-20; 7:18-25

Hebrews 3:13

Ezekiel 14:6; 18:30

STUDY

1. Describe Chuck Colson's sin as a Marine lieutenant on Caribbean maneuvers. (*Loving God* pp. 100-101) Why would such a small act be offensive to God? _____

_____

_____

_____

_____

2. Describe Alypius' battle with sin and evil. (*Loving God*, pp. 103, 104) What critical mistake did he make? _____

_____

"If we say that we have no sin, we are deceiving ourselves and the truth is not in us."

I John 1:8

_____

_____

_____

3. What is your definition of sin? _____

_____

_____

_____

4. Do you consider yourself a sinner? Why? What makes one a sinner? _____

_____

_____

_____

5. Describe the results of sin where you live. How do the people you associate with deceive themselves about sin? How do you? _____

_____

_____

_____

_____

6. Describe the results of sin in someone you know. What is the best way for you to help that person? _____

_____

_____

_____

"We are not sinners because we sin; we sin because we are sinners."

7. Why are Alypius and his experience important in the discussion about sin? _____

R. C. *Sproul*

_____

_____

_____

8. Why is it hard for us to see and deal with our sin? _____

_____

_____

_____

_____

REFLECT

1. Describe something you have done or were tempted to do that parallels Chuck Colson's action as a young Marine.

_____

_____

_____

2. Have you ever been like Alypius? Explain the situation(s) and your reaction(s). _____

_____

_____

_____

3. What do your answers to questions #1 and #2 tell you about yourself? _____

_____

_____

_____

4. Describe some ways you avoid seeing sin in yourself. In what ways do you hide your sins from others? _____

_____

_____

_____

_____

5. How can you keep from deceiving yourself about sin? __

_____

_____

_____

_____

_____

6. Why is it important for you to see your own sin? Is it possible to focus too much on your sin? When? _____

_____

_____

_____

_____

7. What is your response to your own sin? What should it be according to Jesus Christ? _____

_____

_____

_____

_____

SUMMARIZE

What is the most significant lesson you have learned from this study? _____

_____

_____

_____

APPLY

How and when will you apply what you have learned in this study in thought, word or action? _____

_____

_____

_____

_____

". . . In each of us there is sin — not just susceptibility to sin, but sin itself."

Loving God, *page* 101.

PRAY

Spend a few minutes examining your attitudes, actions and relationships over the past month. Confess whatever sins come to mind. Then, consciously thank and praise God for the total forgiveness He promises.

FURTHER STUDY

G. C. Berkouwer, Sin, Wm. B. Eerdmans, 1971.

J. G. Machen, The Christian View of Man, Macmillan, 1939.

Karl Menninger, Whatever Became of Sin?, Hawthorne, 1973.

Theodore Plantinga, Learning to Live with Evil, Wm. B. Eerdmans, 1982.

J. C. Ryle, Holiness, Hunt, 1979. (James Clarke. 1952 — see chapter on sin).

David Myers, The Inflated Self, Seabury Press, 1980.

NOTES

6

"... When You Come Into Your Kingdom"

Christ's death on the cross can be seen from many perspectives: that of the Jewish leaders of the day, the Roman soldiers, the apostles, Pilate, the thieves who died with Him. And, of course, we as Christians must realize that His death is the beginning of His victory.

Because of who Christ is, and through His substitutionary death and bodily resurrection, He purchased our eternal life. Instead of "This is the King of the Jews" nailed on that cross, we can picture our name and our sins nailed there — the crimes for which He was sentenced to death.

Only through His serving that sentence, by His life, love, death and resurrection, are we freed from sin forever. When we believe that truth and repent of our sins, this One who died and is risen saves us from them. The debt for sin has been paid in full by the risen Christ — we are forgiven and utterly cleansed.

READ

Main Readings:

Loving God: Chapter 11 and Chapter 12

Luke 23:13-48

Colossians 2:13, 14

I John 2:1-6

Supplementary Readings:

Ephesians 2:14-16; 4:17-32

Romans 6:23; 8:1, 31-34; 12:1

Acts 3:19

Isaiah 1:16-20

STUDY

1. Describe the events of Christ's trial and death chronologically. (Luke 23) _____

_____

_____

_____

_____

"Without the conviction of the Holy Spirit and the repentance that must follow, there is no way out of our predicament."

Loving God, *page* 121.

2. What role did the thieves play in these events? _____

_____

_____

_____

3. Characterize the thieves' reactions to Jesus. (*Loving God*, Chapter 11) _____

_____

_____

_____

4. How do their reactions to Jesus Christ compare with attitudes you have felt, or things you've heard others say? __

_____

_____

_____

5. For you, what is the significance of Christ's death on the cross? _____

_____

_____

_____

_____

6. What was the most important new truth you learned in the book chapters on the crucifixion account? (*Loving God*, pp. 107-122) _____

_____

_____

7. List some ways you could more fully identify with and understand Jesus' crucifixion. _____

_____

_____

_____

8. Define repentance in your own words. What happens inside a person who repents? What are the noticeable effects of repentance? _____

_____

_____

"... though your sins be as scarlet, they will be as white as snow; though red like crimson, they will be like wool."

Isaiah 1:18

REFLECT

1. Put yourself in the thieves' places. What does Christ's death mean to you as you hang waiting to die? _____

_____

_____

2. List elements of David's and Jacob's attitudes that are similar and/or unlike yours. _____

_____

_____

_____

3. How did you first come to understand the true meaning of repentance? _____

_____

_____

_____

_____

4. Describe the results of repentance that you've experienced in your life. Internally (i.e., attitudes, thoughts) _____

_____

_____

_____

Externally (i.e., actions, reactions) _____

_____

_____

_____

5. What step is repentance in your journey toward loving God? _____

_____

_____

Can a person love God without repenting of sin? Why? Must a person be "sinless" to love God? _____

_____

_____

_____

_____

SUMMARIZE

What is the most significant lesson you have learned from this study? _____

_____

_____

_____

"If there is anything worse than our sin, it is our infinite capacity to rationalize it away."

Loving God, page 120.

APPLY

How and when will you apply what you have learned in this study in thought, word or action? _____

_____

_____

_____

_____

_____

PRAY

Express your thanks to God for sending His Son to die on the cross for you; praise Him for the specific areas of sin for which He has forgiven you.

FURTHER STUDY

James Denny, *The Death of Christ*, Tyndale House, 1951.

C. S. Lewis, *Mere Christianity*, Macmillan, 1943.

John Murray, *Redemption: Accomplished and Applied*, Wm. B. Eerdmans, 1955.

John R. W. Stott, *Basic Christianity*, Inter-Varsity Press, 1958.

B. B. Warfield, *The Person and Work of Christ*, Puritan Reformed Publishing Company, 1950.

NOTES

_____

_____

_____

_____

_____

_____

_____

_____

_____

_____

_____

_____

_____

_____

_____

7
Salt and Light

Holiness is conformity to the character of God and obedience to the will of God. We are to be holy — set apart, different — because God is holy.

God will not tolerate the failure of His chosen ones to treat Him as holy and to be holy themselves. We are to be just because He is just. We are to love because He loves.

As we consider holiness, however, we must understand the relationship between faith and works. Martin Luther said, "You are justified by faith alone, but not by faith that is alone." If faith is not accompanied by works, it is not true faith. No works indicate that there is no faith. One is never saved by works, but if there are no works of obedience to the Lord — a holy life lived in fellowship with Him — there is no salvation.

READ

Main Readings:

Loving God: Chapter 13 and
    Chapter 14

I Peter 1:13-25

James 1:14-27; 2:26

Ephesians 4:17-32

Supplementary Readings:

John 17:14-17

Matthew 5:38-48; 19:21;
    25:40, 45, 46

Colossians 3:12, 13

STUDY

1. Describe the characteristics of holiness illustrated by the following people in the text: Senator William Armstrong, Orv Krieger, Joyce Page, Kenneth Hooker, Donald Adcox, Patti Awan, Mother Teresa. _____

_____

_____

_____

"Mother Teresa ... is not in love with a cause, noble as her cause is ... she loves God and is dedicated to living His life, not her own."

Loving God, page 126.

2. What motivated these people to holiness? _____

_____

_____

_____

3. How was holiness made visible in the Old Testament? In the New Testament? Today? _____

_____

_____

_____

_____

4. In your own words, define holiness. What is it and what is it *not*? _____

_____

_____

_____

5. Was Moses a holy man? Why did God discipline him? __

_____

_____

_____

6. Why and how does God discipline us when we are disobedient? _____

_____

_____

_____

7. What is God's responsibility in man's personal holiness? What is man's responsibility? _____

_____

_____

_____

_____

"Our progress in holiness depends on God and ourselves — on God's grace and on our will to be holy."

Mother Teresa

REFLECT

1. Describe some people you know who exemplify holiness. What things do these people have in common? _____

_____

_____

_____

_____

2. Compare Mother Teresa's life and attitudes to your own. _____

_____

_____

_____

_____

3. What is a proper measurement of personal holiness? ___

_____

_____

_____

4. List some ways in which you are living a holy life. _____

_____

_____

_____

5. List some areas in your life that stand in the way of your personal holiness. _____

_____

_____

_____

6. What things help you live a holy life? _____

_____

_____

_____

SUMMARIZE

What is the most significant lesson you have learned from this study? _____

_____

_____

_____

_____

_____

APPLY

How and when will you apply what you have learned in this study in thought, word or action? _____

_____

_____

_____

_____

". . . you are
to be perfect
as your
heavenly Father
is perfect."

Matthew 5:48

PRAY

Think of three practical ways you could more fully obey Jesus' instruction to be holy. Ask God to help you act on each in the next week — and to help you determine what choices you will make to be obedient to Him.

FURTHER STUDY

Jerry Bridges, *Pursuit of Holiness*, Nav Press, 1982.

Richard Lovelace, *Dynamics of Spiritual Life*, Inter-Varsity Press, 1979.

John Murray, *Principles of Conduct*, Wm. B. Eerdmans, 1957.

A. W. Pink, *The Doctrine of Sanctification*, Reiner, 1966.

K. Prior, *The Way of Holiness*, Inter-Varsity Press, 1967.

J. C. Ryle, *Holiness*, Hunt, 1879, (James Clark, 1952)

R. C. Sproul, "Holiness" series of six cassette tapes. Ligonier Valley Study Center, Stahlstown, PA 15687.

NOTES

8
Justice, Kindness, Humility

When we conform to the character of God and live in obedience to Him, we take on His perspectives, His principles, His standards. But as we pursue holiness, we encounter issues, concerns and tough problems that extend to our families, communities and society.

What does God require of His disciples? To do justice, to love mercy and walk humbly with Him. We do not live holy lives for God in a vacuum. Our corporate holiness is the outworking of the holiness of individuals, of course, but also of the Body of Christ — the Church, the fellowship of the twice-born.

Our corporate holiness is often the clearest statement to the world about the character of the God we serve. When our hearts beat with the heart of God, we share His compassion, His passion for justice and righteousness. And as we live out those concerns, no matter what the visible result, no matter what the cost, we most often set ourselves in direct opposition to the ways of the world. But holy living is required of us — for we serve a holy God who demands that we be like Him.

READ

Main Readings:

Loving God: Chapter 15

Hebrews 12:14-17

Amos 5:11-24

Philippians 2:12-18; 3:8-16

Ezekiel 20:11-14

Jeremiah 18:7-10; 7:8-15; 48:11

Micah 6:8

Supplementary Readings:

Exodus 20-23

Jonah 3:5, 10

II Chronicles 12:6, 7

Hosea 14:1, 2

Isaiah 5:4-7

STUDY

1. How did God make His will known to the Old Testament figures? _____

_____

_____

_____

_____

"Christianity is
abiding by
biblical
standards of
personal
holiness
and in turn
seeking
to bring
holiness
into the
society in
which
we live."

Loving God,
page 146.

2. In what ways is God's will revealed today? For you, what is the clearest way to find God's will? _____

_____

_____

_____

_____

_____

3. What is corporate holiness? _____

_____

_____

_____

_____

4. What is the individual's responsibility and role in corporate holiness? In corporate sin? _____

_____

_____

_____

_____

5. Describe some visible results of corporate sin in your neighborhood. _____

_____

_____

_____

_____

REFLECT

1. Do you feel responsible for your country's sins? Why or why not? _____

_____

_____

_____

_____

2. Do you feel responsible for some corporate sins, but not others? Explain. _____

_____

_____

_____

_____

"God holds man responsible not only for his individual sins but for the corporate sins of society."

3. What is your role in corporate sin? In corporate holiness? _____

Loving God, *page* 142.

_____

_____

_____

_____

4. How does your understanding of corporate sin and holiness help you in your pilgrimage toward loving God? _____

_____

_____

_____

_____

SUMMARIZE

What is the most significant lesson you have learned from this study? _____

_____

_____

_____

_____

"Seek good and not evil, that you may live . . ."

Amos 5:14

APPLY

How and when will you apply what you have learned in this study in thought, word or action? _____

_____

_____

_____

_____

PRAY

In your opinion, what is the greatest way our society sins against those who are helpless? Intercede to God on their behalf, and confess your part in that corporate sin.

FURTHER STUDY

L. Gilkey, *How Can the Church Minister to the World without Losing Herself?*, Harper & Row, 1961.

Carl F. H. Henry, *Aspects of Christian Social Ethics*, Baker Books, 1980.

Carl F. H. Henry, *A Plea for Evangelical Demonstration*.

H. R. Niebuhr, *Christ and Culture*, Harper, 1951.

William Wilberforce, *Real Christianity*, Regal Books, 1982. (James Houston, ed.)

NOTES

9
Taking a Stand

Although loving God is initiated as a personal commitment and concern between a Christian and the Lord Jesus, our love and obedience to Him may require us to stand publicly for own beliefs. Whether it be in a courtroom, in a school system, in a business office or a religious body, the true follower of Christ must uphold Christ's principles and standards no matter what the opposition.

Standing against the world is often costly, but as believers we must be able to see when the will of the majority is at odds with the will of God, and then take our stand for Him. To do so we need to be discerning, rooted in God's Word, so we know His will. As Christians through the ages have had the courage to step out for Christ and the principles of His kingdom — often alone, usually against insurmountable odds — they have actually changed the world.

If we are willing to demonstrate the same courage and commitment, we too can bring change to our world — in whatever arena where God has placed us.

READ

Main Readings:

Loving God: Chapter 16 and
    Chapter 17

Acts 4:18-20; 5:27-29

Romans 13:1-7

Supplementary Readings:

Daniel 3:1-18

Matthew 5:19

I Peter 2:13-23

II Kings 5:8-19

Hebrews 11:23

STUDY

1. Describe the basic elements of Harry Fred Palmer's court case. (*Loving God*, pp. 147-156) ⎯⎯⎯⎯⎯⎯⎯⎯

⎯⎯⎯⎯⎯⎯⎯⎯⎯⎯⎯⎯⎯⎯⎯⎯⎯⎯⎯⎯⎯⎯⎯⎯⎯

⎯⎯⎯⎯⎯⎯⎯⎯⎯⎯⎯⎯⎯⎯⎯⎯⎯⎯⎯⎯⎯⎯⎯⎯⎯

"Believers today have many ancestral radicals in their family tree. In fact, the kingdom of God is full of them."

Loving God, page 165.

2. Explain the crux of Judge Bontrager's dilemma. (*Loving God*, pp. 156-164) ⎯⎯⎯⎯⎯⎯⎯⎯⎯⎯⎯⎯⎯⎯

⎯⎯⎯⎯⎯⎯⎯⎯⎯⎯⎯⎯⎯⎯⎯⎯⎯⎯⎯⎯⎯⎯⎯⎯⎯

⎯⎯⎯⎯⎯⎯⎯⎯⎯⎯⎯⎯⎯⎯⎯⎯⎯⎯⎯⎯⎯⎯⎯⎯⎯

⎯⎯⎯⎯⎯⎯⎯⎯⎯⎯⎯⎯⎯⎯⎯⎯⎯⎯⎯⎯⎯⎯⎯⎯⎯

⎯⎯⎯⎯⎯⎯⎯⎯⎯⎯⎯⎯⎯⎯⎯⎯⎯⎯⎯⎯⎯⎯⎯⎯⎯

3. If you were in Bill Bontrager's position, what would you have done? List the key ingredients in making a decision for such a risky action. ⎯⎯⎯⎯⎯⎯⎯⎯⎯⎯⎯⎯⎯⎯

⎯⎯⎯⎯⎯⎯⎯⎯⎯⎯⎯⎯⎯⎯⎯⎯⎯⎯⎯⎯⎯⎯⎯⎯⎯

⎯⎯⎯⎯⎯⎯⎯⎯⎯⎯⎯⎯⎯⎯⎯⎯⎯⎯⎯⎯⎯⎯⎯⎯⎯

4. How does a Christian know when it is time to take a stand publicly, and when it is right to remain silent? ⎯⎯⎯⎯⎯

⎯⎯⎯⎯⎯⎯⎯⎯⎯⎯⎯⎯⎯⎯⎯⎯⎯⎯⎯⎯⎯⎯⎯⎯⎯

⎯⎯⎯⎯⎯⎯⎯⎯⎯⎯⎯⎯⎯⎯⎯⎯⎯⎯⎯⎯⎯⎯⎯⎯⎯

5. When would it be right for a Christian to be involved in civil disobedience? Would you ever participate? Under what specific circumstances? ⎯⎯⎯⎯⎯⎯⎯⎯⎯⎯⎯⎯⎯⎯

⎯⎯⎯⎯⎯⎯⎯⎯⎯⎯⎯⎯⎯⎯⎯⎯⎯⎯⎯⎯⎯⎯⎯⎯⎯

⎯⎯⎯⎯⎯⎯⎯⎯⎯⎯⎯⎯⎯⎯⎯⎯⎯⎯⎯⎯⎯⎯⎯⎯⎯

_____

_____

6. If Christians must disobey someone in authority, what should be the attitude in which it is done? Why? _____

_____

_____

7. What was Christ's attitude when He suffered injustice at the hands of the state? _____

_____

_____

_____

8. List common characteristics of radical Christians like: William Wilberforce, Dietrich Bonhoeffer, Daniel, Shadrach, Meshach and Abednego. Describe other radical Christians you have known. _____

_____

_____

_____

_____

9. List issues over which Christians you know (including yourself) should be taking a stand but are not. Explain why and how. _____

_____

_____

_____

_____

"Every one who shall confess me before men, I will also confess him before My Father who is in heaven, but whoever shall deny Me before men, I will also deny him before My Father who is in heaven."

Matthew 10: 32, 33

REFLECT

1. Describe some circumstances when you've seen God's standards compromised. How did you react? What were the consequences? _____

_____

_____

_____

2. Have you ever taken a stand for Christ? What happened? Describe your feelings. Were there hurdles you had to overcome? _____

_____

_____

_____

_____

3. List Scripture passages that relate to hesitance to take a stand for Christ. _____

"If we would love God, we must love His justice and act upon it."

Loving God, *page* 172.

_____

_____

_____

4. When and for what reasons do you need to take a stand for Christ in your neighborhood or area? _____

_____

_____

_____

At your work? _____

_____

_____

_____

At your church? _____

_____

_____

_____

In your home? _____

_____

_____

_____

SUMMARIZE

What is the most significant lesson you have learned from this study? _____

_____

_____

_____

APPLY

How and when will you apply what you have learned in this study in thought, word or action? _____

_____

_____

_____

_____

PRAY

What one area of your life would you like great boldness for expressing your commitment to Jesus Christ? Ask God to give you the courage to stand up for Him at the next opportunity.

FURTHER STUDY

O. Cullmann, *The State in the New Testament*, Scribner, 1965.

Mark O. Hatfield, *Between a Rock and a Hard Place*, Word Books, 1977.

Jon Johnston, *Will Evangelicalism Survive Its Own Popularity?*, Zondervan, 1980.

Garth Lean, *Strangely Warmed*, Tyndale House, 1979.

Malcolm Muggeridge, *The End of Christendom*, Wm. B. Eerdmans, 1980.

Francis Schaeffer, *The Christian Manifesto*, Crossway, 1981.

Howard Synder, *The Radical Wesley*, Inter-Varsity Press, 1980.

John Telford, ed., *The Letters of the Rev. John Wesley*, The Epworth Press, 1931.

NOTES

10
A Fellowship of Suffering

The Church is meant to care for others out of obedience to Christ, to heal those who hurt, to take away fear, to proclaim and to practice the Good News. We are also to restore community and live in fellowship with one another. We give visibility to Christ's Kingdom in the world today. This is the Church on the front lines.

In Hebrews we are urged to "go outside the camp" — outside our own religious community — with a willingness to be criticized if need be, as was our Lord. Our faith is in word only if we neglect sharing and doing good for those in need. As James says, "pure and undefiled religion" not only means keeping oneself unstained by the world, but also ministering to those in need — the "widows and orphans" among us.

Christians are set apart — a holy nation. As the people of God, we have a new identity. But only if we see ourselves in this identity can we act according to it. If we truly understand the fact that we *are* a holy nation, we will live that out, and proclaim — not only with words, but with deeds — God's Good News to a world in desperate spiritual and physical need.

READ

Main Readings:

Loving God: Chapter 18,
    Chapter 19, and Chapter 20

Matthew 25:31-46

I Peter 2:9

Philippians 3:1-16

Supplementary Readings:

Hebrews 13:2, 12-16

James 1:27

Luke 14:12-14

I Corinthians 12:26

STUDY

1. Describe ways that the following expressed their identity as citizens of a holy nation: Full Gospel Church of Seoul, Korea; Eastminster Presbyterian Church in Wichita, Kansas; Janice Webb, Mildred Taylor and the volunteers at Agape House; Judge Clement. _____

_____

_____

_____

_____

2. List the common characteristics of those discussed in Question #1. Do you see these characteristics in others around you who identify themselves as citizens of a holy nation? Describe those people. _____

_____

_____

_____

"They love one another . . . They don't consider themselves brothers in the usual sense, but brothers instead through the Spirit, in God."

Aristides, describing early Christians.

3. What is the fellowship of suffering? Describe God's "Holy Nation." How do the two relate to each other? _____

_____

_____

_____

_____

_____

4. Why aren't all Christians involved on the front lines? ___

_____

_____

_____

5. What is the solution to that situation? Is such a solution necessary? _____

_____

_____

_____

6. What would be the result if all Christians participated in the suffering of others? _____

_____

_____

_____

"Not until we go where need is and share in the suffering of the poor, alienated, isolated, and downtrodden will the holy nation of God's people also become the loving nation."

Loving God, page 182.

REFLECT

1. What things indicate to yourself and others that you are a citizen of God's Holy Nation? What could you do to more fully distinguish yourself as a citizen of God's Holy Nation? _____

_____

_____

_____

_____

2. Have you been part of the fellowship of suffering? Explain. _____

_____

_____

_____

_____

_____

3. List the biggest fears you have or obstacles you face that keep you from sharing others' suffering. _____

_____

_____

_____

_____

_____

4. What would Jesus Christ tell you about those fears or obstacles? List Scripture passages that apply. _____

_____

_____

_____

_____

_____

5. How do the Holy Nation and the fellowship of suffering affect your life? _____

_____

_____

_____

SUMMARIZE

What is the most significant lesson you have learned from this study? _____

_____

_____

_____

APPLY

How and when will you apply what you have learned in this study in thought, word or action? _____

_____

_____

_____

_____

_____

"Our presence in a place of need is more powerful than a thousand sermons. Being there is our witness. And until we are, our orthodoxy and doctrine are mere words; our liturgies and gospel choruses ring hollow."

PRAY

Express yourself to God concerning your greatest area of suffering; ask for His help. Then, pray for someone you know who is suffering for following Jesus.

Loving God,
page 192.

FURTHER STUDY

Thom Hopler, A World of Difference: Following Christ Beyond Your Cultural Walls, Inter-Varsity Press, 1981.

Jay Kesler, Growing Places, Revell, 1978.

Hans Kung, The Church, Sheed and Ward, 1967.

Herbert Lockyer, Dark Threads the Weaver Needs, Revell, 1979.

Leslie Newbigin, The Household of God: Lectures on the Nature of the Church, Friendship, 1954.

Charles R. Swindoll, Hand Me Another Brick, Thomas Nelson, 1978.

Philip Yancey, Where Is God When It Hurts?, Zondervan, 1977.

59

NOTES

11
The Visible Church

Christ promises that the Church will not be destroyed, that "the gates of hell shall not prevail against it." But whether the Church functions as a dynamic force or an elite social club in today's society depends on the commitment of its members to Christ and willingness to live as He lived.

It is as Christians understand and live out obedience, faith, suffering, holiness that the Church will become the powerful instrument of hope and change it can be in our world. As long as Christians live day to day more concerned about their own spiritual entertainment, or the size of their sanctuaries and the furniture in the fellowship hall, the needy multitudes will remain outside.

But when the Church functions as the vital organism God intends it to be, we will no longer expect those in need to come to us, but we will go to them. That's what Jesus did — and that's how His Church will bring His message to the world today.

READ

Main Readings:

Loving God: Chapter 21

Matthew 16:18, 19

Exodus 19:5, 6; 29:43-46

John 1:4-14

Supplementary Readings:

John 17

Deuteronomy 12:11

I Peter 2:9

James 1

STUDY

1. Describe the conditions of the POWs discussed in Chapter 21 of *Loving God*. _____

_____

_____

_____

"Relying on Him, they had nothing less than the privilege of showing the Lord's death, burial and resurrection . . . in what otherwise was a living hell."

Loving God, *page 206.*

2. What was the significance of the woman in the crowd who gave the cookie away? _____

_____

_____

_____

3. What is most striking to you about the members of the POW Church? _____

_____

_____

_____

4. What do you think Jeff Powell, Terry Jones, James Kasler, Norman McDaniel, James Ray, Howard Rutledge, Harry Jenkins and Tom Curtis would say to the American Church? To your church? _____

_____

_____

_____

5. How did these men resist their captors? _____

_____

_____

_____

6. Are there situations that exist today — not necessarily related to war — in which you must resist outside forces? Explain. _____

_____

_____

_____

_____

7. What characteristics of the POW Church are needed in your local church? _____

_____

_____

_____

_____

8. How can Christians in America learn some of the same lessons and truths that the POW Church learned? _____

_____

_____

_____

REFLECT

1. Have you ever been persecuted for any reason? Describe the circumstances. _____

_____

_____

_____

_____

2. How did you react? _____

_____

_____

_____

3. Describe the times in your life when your faith in God has been the most real to you. _____

_____

_____

_____

4. Under what circumstances has your faith grown the most? Why? _____

"It would have
been easy
to lose his
faith, but
sometimes,
mysteriously,
he felt he was
not along."

_____

_____

_____

Loving God,
page 201.

5. What conclusions can you draw about the kind of life you should live to keep your faith growing and vital? _____

_____

_____

_____

6. Are you living that kind of life now? Why or why not? If not, what can you do about it? _____

_____

_____

_____

_____

_____

SUMMARIZE

What is the most significant lesson you have learned from this study? _____

_____

_____

_____

_____

_____

". . . Through many tribulations we must enter into the Kingdom of God."

Acts 14:22

APPLY

How and when will you apply what you have learned in this study in thought, word or action? _____

_____

_____

_____

_____

_____

_____

_____

PRAY

Choose one circumstance where you are currently struggling to exercise faith. Ask God to help you trust Him more than you have ever done before as you go through the experience.

FURTHER STUDY

Edmund P. Clowney, *The Doctrine of the Church*, Presbyterian Reform Pub. Co., 1969.

Richard Halverson, *The Timelessness of Christ*, Regal Books, 1982.

Bruce Milne, *We Belong Together*, Inter-Varsity Press.

Howard Rutledge, *In the Presence of Mine Enemies*, Revell, 1973.

Francis Schaeffer, *The Church Before the Watching World*, Inter-Varsity Press, 1971.

Howard Snyder, *The Community of the King*, Inter-Varsity Press, 1977.

Howard Snyder, *The Problem of Wineskins: Church Renewal in Technological Age*, Inter-Varsity Press, 1975.

NOTES

12
Death Into Life

One only has to look through the gospels to see Christ's great compassion for the broken, hurting and hopeless. As followers and imitators of Christ, we can do no less. Not only does He care about our own needs, He demands that we follow His example and care about others who feel neglected, unloved, useless.

It is as we give of Christ's love in us that we fully understand God's grace. We will not only have received mercy from our Lord, but we will have the opportunity of offering it to others because of Him.

Again, we can only do that if we have first experienced the central paradox of the Christian faith — losing our lives for Christ's sake in order to find life. As we die to self, God is able to use us as willing vessels for His service. It is only as obedient servants that we can truly live out the day to day reality of loving Him. And that's what the Christian life is all about.

READ

Main Readings:

Loving God: Chapter 22

I Corinthians 15:58; 16:13, 14

Hebrews 6:9-12, 18-20

Ephesians 5:1-20

I Timothy 4:6-16

Supplementary Readings:

Matthew 13:18-23

II Peter 3:14-18

III John 1:11

Ephesians 4

STUDY

1. List important facts about Myrtie Howell's life. _____

_____

_"Therefore, be
imitators
of God
as beloved
children."_

Ephesians 5:1

_____

_____

_____

2. What triggered her depression? _____

_____

_____

_____

3. How was her spirit and faith restored? _____

_____

_____

_____

4. Contrast Myrtie's life before and after her encounter with God when she received the directive to "write to prisoners." _____

_____

_____

_____

5. List lessons or spiritual truths that can be learned from Myrtie's life and experience. _____

_____

_____

_____

_____

6. Discuss other circumstances or people's lives through which you have seen these same truths or lessons. _____

_____

_____

_____

7. How do these issues relate to loving God? _____

_____

_____

_____

REFLECT

1. Have you ever felt like Myrtie did — ready to give up? Explain. _____

_____

_____

_____

"Myrtie had recognized the vanity and purposelessness of life without God; the emptiness of life lived for self."

Loving God, *page 215.*

2. How was your situation resolved? What lessons did you learn as a result? _____

_____

_____

_____

_____

3. Are you mindful of these lessons when things are going well, when you weren't discouraged? Should you? Why? __

_____

_____

_____

_____

_____

4. Have these situations helped you learn to love God? How? _____

_____

"Once I turned
over my life
to Him —
I mean
really did it —   5. List some results of your love for God that have been
He took care   visible in the last month. _____
of all
my needs."   _____

Myrtie Howell   _____

6. List the gifts or talents you have that you are using for God. _____

_____

_____

_____

7. List some other creative ways you could use your gifts or talents for God's glory in the next six months. _____

_____

_____

_____

_____

8. How could you stimulate others to begin using their gifts? _____

_____

_____

_____

SUMMARIZE

What is the most significant lesson you have learned from this study? _____

_____

_____

_____

_____

"God don't need no quitters."

Loving God, *page* 214.

APPLY

How and when will you apply what you have learned in this study in thought, word or action? _____

_____

_____

_____

_____

PRAY

Thank God for each of the talents and abilities He has given you. Ask Him to show you new and creative ways you could put them to use for His glory.

FURTHER STUDY

Evelyn Christenson, *Gaining Through Losing*, Victor Books, 1980.

Morris A. Inch, *My Servant Job*, Baker, 1979.

David C. Needham, *Birthright*, Multnomah Press, 1979.

Luis Palau, *The Moment to Shout*, Multnomah Press, 1979.

William J. Peterson, *The Discipling of Timothy*, Victor Books, 1980.

William E. Thorn, *Catch the Little Foxes that Spoil the Vine*, Revell, 1980.

NOTES

13
Living in the Arena

The Christian life — the life of one who loves God — is a struggle to be faithful. The foundation of that faithful life is Jesus Christ. He is to be more important than anything else. All other things are worthless compared to knowing Him, His power and the fellowship of His sufferings.

Most Christians would subscribe to that belief, of course, but the real business of loving God does not take place in the abstract. Theology must be lived — and faithful obedience to Christ often involves tough choices.

But if we aren't willing to make those choices and prefer instead to live our lives within comfortable — and safe — confines, we miss out on the far greater experience. "I count all things to be loss in view of the surpassing value of knowing Christ Jesus my Lord," wrote Paul.

As we share the great apostle's attitude, we too will attain the "prize of the upward call of God in Christ Jesus."

READ

Main Readings:

Loving God: Epilogue

Philippians 3

Matthew 5:1-20; 6:24, 25

Hebrews 3

Supplementary Readings:

I Thessalonians 4:1-5:11

James 4

John 15

STUDY

1. Describe the main characters in the Epilogue: Dave Chapman, Jack Newman. _____

_____

_____

2. What was Dave Chapman's understanding of Christianity at the opening of the text? _____

_____

_____

3. Outline the stages of Dave's walk with Christ. _____

_____

_____

_____

4. What enabled Dave to go on with his faith? What held him back? _____

_____

_____

5. What did faithfulness to God cost Dave? Explain. _____

_____

_____

6. What important lessons did Dave learn during his struggle to love God? _____

_____

_____

7. In what ways do such struggles help Christians learn to love God? _____

_____

_____

_____

8. What would you do if you were in Dave Chapman's situation at the close of the book, and why? _____

_____

_____

_____

REFLECT

1. How does Dave's walk with Christ compare and contrast to yours? _____

_____

_____

_____

_____

"To one who knows the right thing to do and does not do it, to him it is sin."

James 4:17

2. Describe similar struggles you've had with your faith, and the results. _____

_____

_____

_____

3. Summarize the history of your walk with Christ. _____

_____

_____

_____

_____

4. What are the three most important lessons you've learned about yourself and your faith through this study? _

_____

_____

_____

_____

5. Describe how these lessons will help you love God more. _____

"For me to live
is Christ,
and to
die is gain."

_____

_____

Philippians
1:21

_____

_____

_____

6. Explain where you are in your pilgrimage toward loving God. _____

_____

_____

_____

_____

_____

Where are you heading? _____

_____

_____

_____

_____

SUMMARIZE

What is the most significant lesson you have learned from
this study? _____

_____

_____

_____

_____

_____

_____

APPLY

How and when will you apply what you have learned in this
study in thought, word or action? _____

_____

_____

_____

_____

_____

_____

PRAY

Think of the specific, practical ways you could re-
vive your desire to love God with all your heart, soul,
mind and strength. Ask the Holy Spirit to fill you
with power to begin accomplishing these things.

FURTHER STUDY

Augustine, *City of God*, Image Books, 1958. (Gerald Walsh and Grace Monahan, translators)

John Bunyan, *The Pilgrim's Progress*, Signet, 1964.

Hannah Whitall Smith, *The Christian's Secret of a Happy Life*, Revell, 1952.

William Wilberforce, *Real Christianity*, Regal, 1982. (James Houston, ed.)

J. C. Ryle, *Practical Religion*, Baker Books, 1977.

Martyn Lloyd-Jones, *Spiritual Depression: Its Causes and Cures*, Wm. B. Eerdmans, 1965.
Martyn Lloyd-Jones, *Studies in Sermon on the Mount*, Wm. B. Eerdmans, 1971.

J. Oswald Sanders, *Spiritual Leadership*, Moody, 1974.

J. C. Ryle, *Christian Leaders of the 18th Century*, Banner of Truth, 1981.

NOTES

_____

_____

_____

_____

_____

_____

_____

_____

_____

_____

Loving God Summary Statement

This study guide and your reading of *Loving God* will serve little purpose unless they evoke a deeper understanding of what Jesus meant when he instructed us to "love the Lord your God with all your heart, soul and mind" — and how you plan to apply that understanding to action.

Use the space below to summarize the things from this study that have particularly hit home. Be specific in describing your insights; think about how God may be speaking to you regarding particular areas of your life.

Loving God Action Statement

Having summarized your thoughts, take a few minutes to write down specific ways you can act on Jesus' command to love God with all that you are. What changes in lifestyle should you implement? What can you do this week to love God more fully?

_____

_____

_____

_____

_____

_____

_____

_____

_____

_____

_____

_____

_____

_____

_____

_____

_____

_____

_____

_____